THE BALL
DEVON ANI

An Introduction by the Ba

Dedicated to the memory of Claude Pike O.B.E.
(1915–2002)

Queen's Ware (cream coloured earthenware).
Pierced chestnut basket. Wedgwood *c.* 1774
Image by courtesy Wedgwood Museum Trust, Barlaston, Staffordshire

ISBN 1 900147 300   First published 2003
© The Ball Clay Heritage Society, Newton Abbot
www.clayheritage.org

Note: Illustrations in this book are from the Ball Clay Heritage Society collection
except where otherwise acknowledged.

CORNISH
HILLSIDE
PUBLICATIONS

Front cover: 'Crab' crane at the head of a shaft at WBB's Preston Manor Works, Kingsteignton
in 1950. George Frost (ganger) and Sid Carnell (trammer) transferring the contents of a bucket raised
from the mine into a wagon that will be hauled up a 'high back' from which the clay will be tipped
onto an outside clay heap.

A seam of ball clay being worked by Felix 'Nobby' Vallance using a pneumatic spader in an underground mine with timber supports, *c*. 1950.

1
What is Ball Clay?

Ball clays are found in articles used daily by millions of people around the world – usually without them realising it! They are essential components of most types of pottery. They are easily mouldable and are white or near white when fired at a high temperature: ball clays are truly 'fine ceramic clays'.

The name 'ball clay' derives from the former method of winning the clay by cutting it from the floor of an open pit in cubes. Because of the clay's high plasticity the cubes held together, but after being handled several times the corners became knocked in and the cubes turned into balls – so, to the potters, a plastic, white-firing clay was a 'ball clay'.

Unlike china clays – with which they are sometimes confused – ball clays are rather rare in the world.

What are probably the world's most important deposits are found in Devon and Dorset. Ball clays from these deposits have been used by manufacturers of white-bodied pottery since the days of the famous 18th century potters such as Josiah Wedgwood, Astbury and Spode. Nowadays these ball clays are shipped to over 80 countries around the world to the manufacturers of tableware, washbasins and toilet bowls, wall and floor tiles, electrical insulators and other ceramics.

Ball clays consist of ultra fine clay particles. This helps to make them sticky (or 'plastic') and easily shaped when damp (the word 'clay' is derived from the Old English 'claeg', meaning sticky). Some also have fluid properties that are valuable in the casting of large ceramic pieces such as toilet bowls. Like china clays (which are also called 'kaolins'), English ball clays contain a large proportion of the mineral kaolinite and fire hard in the potter's kiln. However, china clay particles are coarser. Consequently, unlike ball clays, china clays are not very plastic.

Most types of 'whiteware' pottery contain both ball clay and china clay. The ball clay helps to shape the piece, adding 'green' strength to the body before firing, whilst china clay provides extra whiteness.

2
How the Ball Clay Deposits Occurred

A rare coincidence of geological conditions was required to form and preserve the ball clay deposits: suitable kaolinite-rich source rocks largely free of iron oxides, erosion of these rocks into fresh or brackish water 'traps' for the ultra fine particles before they could be washed out to sea, and no subsequent erosion or deep burial of the resultant sedimentary deposit.

The Wareham Basin

The deposits in Dorset, the Wareham Basin, were formed about 45 million years ago in the Eocene epoch of the Tertiary period when the climate was sub tropical and wet. Sediments from deeply weathered uplands in Devon and Somerset (that have long since gone) were carried eastwards by a great meandering river. The sediments were

Artist's impression of landscape believed to be similar to that in which the Wareham Clay basin was formed.
IPR/34-12C British Geological Survey. © NERC. All rights reserved.

deposited in deltas and lagoons spread over an extensive area – about 55 square miles (150 square km) – near Wareham where the fresh water met the sea-filled Hampshire Basin. The coarser and heavier 'Bagshot Sands' settled easily. Vitally, the semi-saline, brackish conditions helped ultra fine clay particles to settle quickly as well, before they could be washed on out to sea. In the sea they would have been so contaminated with salts that their properties would have changed, making them useless for most ceramics.

Subsequently the great Alpine mountain building forces lifted up the underlying chalk, ending the formation of the deposit and creating the Purbeck Hills that now hem in the Wareham deposit along its southern boundary.

The Bovey and Petrockstowe Basins

The two Devon deposits, the Bovey Basin between Newton Abbot and Bovey Tracey in South Devon and the Petrockstowe Basin between Peters Marland and Meeth in North Devon, were formed somewhat later, about 30 million years ago in the Oligocene period of the Tertiary. The hot, wet climatic conditions were continuing, as was the erosion of the region's deeply weathered uplands. However, now, a massive fault known as the Sticklepath-Lustleigh Fault Zone was opening up, running north-west to south-east from near Bideford to Torquay. This fault created depressions in which swampy, fresh water lakes formed – and into which the sediment from the surrounding uplands was washed. Rivers carrying sediments from different uplands entered the lakes at different points, dropping first the heavier sands and sandy clays and then the finer clays.

Back swamps formed in the quieter areas of the lakes with rafts of floating vegetation and trees (including sequoia) – akin to the Florida Everglades of today. As the vegetation decayed it created organic acids that were essential for ensuring that the ultra fine clay particles that were washed into the basins settled quickly and were not carried on out to sea. Often, fine carbon from the decaying vegetation mixed with the settling clays, helping to give them some of their unique plastic and fluid properties. Ball clays with a high carbon content look brown or black, but the carbon burns off in the potter's kiln leaving a white or near white ceramic.

In some situations in the Bovey Basin the swamp vegetation was so abundant that it led to the creation of thick beds of carbonaceous

E.C.C. Ball Clay's Newbridge pit near Chudleigh Knighton, in 1990, showing a
cross-section of the many seams of light-coloured clays or sands and dark
lignitic clays or lignites deposited in the Bovey Basin.
Photograph courtesy of Colin Bristow.

lignite. This 'Bovey Coal' has at times served as a brown coal fuel and is now used in horticulture as an alternative to peat.

As the Sticklepath Fault developed over millions of years, the earliest beds of sediment remained near the surface where they rested against the 'rims' of the basins, but they gradually slumped in the centre of the basins. The Bovey Basin is over 4,000 feet (1,300 metres) deep and about 7 miles long by 5 miles wide at its widest point (11 km by 8 km). The Petrockstowe Basin is much smaller: about 2,300 feet (700 metres) deep, only 4½ miles (7 km) long and less than one mile (1.5 km) wide. The great depth of these basins (compared with the highest point on Dartmoor today at about 2,000 feet (620 metres)!) allowed a very large number of beds to be laid down, dipping towards the centre.

Sands, Lignites – and Ball Clays!

Some of the beds or 'seams' in the three deposits in Devon and Dorset are mainly quartz sand. Some in Devon are almost entirely lignite. Many others contain a mixture of fine clay minerals (particularly kaolinite) with proportions of quartz and carbon that vary across the deposit, depending on the proximity of the incoming river and any back swamps. The nature of the clay minerals in the mix depends mainly on the source rock from which they were derived. It was crucial that the deep weathering of the source rocks eliminated almost all iron oxides. These oxides have caused the majority of clay deposits around the world to be coloured red, brown or yellow – as such, they are mainly suitable for making bricks and items such as sewage pipes and terracotta pottery – but not whitewares.

The relatively shallow Wareham deposits are less complex than the others and are largely free of lignite. As a result of erosion, the original deposits, up to about 500 feet (150 metres) deep, are now mostly confined to separate 'lenses' several acres in extent in which the clay is about 15 to 50 feet (5 to 15 metres) thick in, at most, four or five rather thick seams beneath overburden of 10 to 200 feet (3 to 60 metres). From the whole deposit about 26 different clay types are produced. The source rocks have given rise to clay minerals with a very fine particle size – giving high green strength – and a pale ivory to buff colour when fired. These properties are ideal for floor and wall tiles, but the clays are also used as components in most other types of ceramic.

In the Petrockstowe Basin the clay minerals were derived from a single source, the Culm Shale uplands of mid Devon. In their resultant high green strength and ivory to buff fired colour these clays typically resemble Wareham clays – and therefore are ideal for the production of tiles and large electrical insulators. However, the Petrockstowe Basin is complex with a large number of clay types, many of which also include carbon. This gives them particular properties making them especially valuable as components in other fine ceramic applications.

In the case of the Bovey Basin, the predominant kaolinite clay mineral was derived from a variety of source rocks in the uplands surrounding the Basin. Where the source was china clay (or 'kaolin') from the deeply weathered granite mountains of Dartmoor, the resultant ball clays tend to be like china clay: coarse grained (and therefore not very plastic) but white-firing. Where the source of kaolinite was other rocks, the clays tend to be finer grained (and therefore more plastic) but off white to creamy white in colour when fired.

These important variations in clay mineral, combined with the presence of carbon and quartz in certain seams and the very large number of relatively thin beds, have resulted in a huge number of permutations and more than 250 clay types – the largest range of any ball clay deposit in the world.

Traditionally, Bovey Basin ball clays have been divided into two broad groups. Firstly, whiter-firing 'potters'' clays, often containing a significant amount of carbon that enhances their plasticity. These were called 'black', 'dark blue' or 'light blue' clays, depending on the colour when dug: they are sometimes regarded as the 'true' ball clays. Secondly, less white-firing and less plastic 'stoneware' clays that contain little or no carbon but an appreciable amount of fine quartz sand (these clays are often referred to as 'brokes' – because the non-sticky quartz causes them to break up readily).

Today, the different types of clay are blended to obtain the properties ideal for each ceramic application. The ball clay producer has to identify the properties of each clay seam as they change across the deposit, understand how the clay will behave when formed and fired as part of a ceramic body, and blend together different seams to produce a large number of consistent products suitable for each individual customer's particular manufacturing process.

3
The Widespread Use of Ball Clay

Readers may be surprised to learn that they probably use articles containing Devon or Dorset ball clays every day – whether they are in Britain, elsewhere in Western Europe or in many Middle or Far Eastern countries. This is because ball clay is an important ingredient of tableware such as earthenware and stoneware, in washbasins and toilet bowls, wall and floor tiles and other ceramic articles, as well as being used as a filler in some rubber and plastic products such as garden hoses and car window trims. It is even found in the tiles on the roof of the Sydney Opera House and in the commemorative dinner services presented to US presidents!

Earliest Uses

It is generally accepted that Dorset ball clays – and probably Devon ball clays too – have been used since Roman times to make crude pottery. However it was the introduction of tobacco to England in the 16th century by Sir Walter Raleigh and others, and the need for a suitable clay with which to make tobacco pipes, that led to the start of the modern ball clay trade.

According to a tradition, Sir Walter Raleigh, one of the pioneers of tobacco smoking in the 1550s, smoked his first pipe tobacco at Cornwood in South Devon. The subsequent enormous demand for clay tobacco pipes created the early ball clay industry.

Clay tobacco pipes made in Exeter in the mid 18th century. Tobacco pipe clays from Kingsteignton were carried by packhorse to Exeter, which was a significant centre for the manufacture and export of clay tobacco pipes from about 1675 to 1720 – when it was the third or fourth provincial city in England and the largest port on the south coast.
Image courtesy Exeter Museums

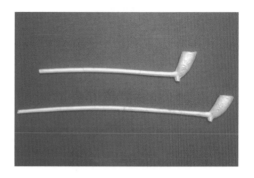

Although the highly plastic ball clays were ideal for tobacco pipe manufacture, their expansion and contraction during firing made them difficult to control in tableware manufacture. Most pottery was made with easy-to-use local coloured clays. By the 17th century it was common for jugs, bowls and other tableware made with these clays to be covered with either a thick white glaze (as in Delft ware) or a white clay slip coating. From at least the 1650s potters in Bideford were using a white slip of North Devon ball clay and scratching designs through the white slip, exposing the coloured body beneath.

Shipments of Dorset tobacco pipe clays from Poole were significant by the 1630's and were the port's most important cargo for most of the 17th and 18th centuries, especially to London and many south coast ports. By 1662 the trade had become sufficiently important for an Act to be passed forbidding the export of pipe clays to foreign countries. Shipments of North Devon clay through Bideford were also important in this period, especially to tobacco pipe manufacturers in Bristol, but shipments of South Devon clays seem to have been relatively small until the middle of the 18th century.

Important 18th Century Developments

Whilst the Chinese learnt how to make fine white porcelain many centuries ago, it was only in the 18th century that European potters learnt how to make good quality white-bodied pottery. They had to overcome the difficulties of using white firing plastic 'tobacco pipe' clays, and had to both discover and learn how to use china clays with little plasticity.

It was the achievements in this area by the famous early potters in Stoke-on-Trent such as Wedgwood, Astbury and Spode that caused

Josiah Wedgwood's most famous achievement in 'Queens Ware' was the
952 piece dinner and dessert service with 'Frog' crests made for the
Empress Catherine the Great of Russia in 1774.
Image by courtesy of the Wedgwood Museum Trust, Barlaston, Staffordshire

the demand for ball clays to take off – along with the demand for
china clays. They all needed ball clays from Devon and Dorset – as
well as china clays from Cornwall and Devon – to make their fine
'cream wares', 'Queen's Ware' and so on. A typical recipe for such
pottery could have included equal quantities of ball clay, china clay,
flint (a form of silica) and Cornish stone (a source of feldspar).
Between 1765 and 1785 – at the same time as the industrial revolu-
tion in the manufacture of pottery and the associated 'canal mania'
– the annual shipments from South Devon quadrupled to almost
10,000 tons.

One of the lesser-known early applications of ball clay was in the
production of a high-grade ceramic known as Coade Stone. This was
first produced in London in 1770 by Eleanor Coade from Lyme Regis.
It was an architectural ceramic of high artistic and technical quality
that has been found to be an exceptionally durable, artificial 'stone'
for building decoration and statuary. Examples include friezes on
Buckingham Palace, fan vaulting in St George's Chapel, Windsor and
the Lion Statue on Westminster Bridge. A recent detailed scientific
analysis of the 'stone' has confirmed that ball clays from Devon or
Dorset were the major component, together with pre-fired clay. Mrs
Coade died in 1825 and production had ceased by about 1840.

A 'Lady's Amusement' pattern earthenware plate made at the Indio Pottery, Bovey Tracey (the forerunner of the Bovey Pottery) c. 1790–1800.

A fine example of Coade Stone: the lion statue on Westminster Bridge – close to the site of Mrs Coade's factory – dated 1837.

Letterheadings of early ball clay customers.

12

International Trade and Local Potteries

By the second half of the 19th century the 1662 ban on exports had been lifted and an increasing proportion of ball clay production was exported to potteries in Europe – from Kuznetsov in St Petersburg to Villeroy & Boch in the Saar, De Porceleyne Fles in Delft and Pickman in Seville. With the development of potteries in the USA and Canada, mainly by potters from Stoke-on-Trent who had been brought up on English ball clays, North America also became a very important market. The English ball clay industry became an extremely cosmopolitan business with a string of long-standing trading relationships that in many cases have continued to the present day.

Thanks to its coalfields and its concentration of potting expertise, the Stoke-on-Trent area has for centuries been the main centre in the UK for ceramic production – and therefore of ball clay usage. However, several important ceramic factories were established close to ball clay production. Some, notably the Bovey Pottery in Bovey Tracey in Devon and Poole Pottery in Dorset, produced tableware on a large scale. Others used the less valuable stoneware clays to produce the pale cream bricks that are a feature of many West Country buildings, as well as drain pipes, chimney pots and wall tiles – notably Candy & Co. (latterly British Ceramic Tile) in Heathfield, Bovey Tracey, Hexter Humpherson in Newton Abbot and the Marland brick works in North Devon.

In the late 19th and early 20th centuries clusters of smaller art potteries were established near the ball clay areas – such as the Watcombe, Torquay Art, Aller Vale and Devon Tor Potteries in South Devon and the Bideford and Barnstaple potteries in North Devon. However, with a few notable exceptions, such as Devonmoor Art Pottery in Liverton, they used mainly red- or brown-firing clays from, for example, Watcombe and Fremington, rather than ball clays.

The following pages contain photographs showing art pottery and the larger scale uses of ball clay in tableware, sanitaryware and tiles.

Toby Jugs produced at the Devonmoor Art Pottery, Liverton, near Bovey Tracey –
which used the local ball clays. Although ball clays are valued because they fire
white or off white, other clays – such as Fremington clays from North Devon
and Watcombe clays from Torquay – are easier to use and therefore
often preferred by art potters.
Image by courtesy of John Hobbs

Removing fired tableware of traditional design from a modern tunnel
kiln at the Spode factory, customers for ball clay since the 18th century.
Image by courtesy of Spode, Stoke-on-Trent

Pieces of sanitaryware – wash basins and toilets – stacked on a kiln car ready for firing in a tunnel kiln. The casting and other properties of ball clay play an important role in the manufacture of such large pieces. Consequently, this is one of the most valuable applications of ball clay.

A bathroom like this, with white bodied ceramic wall tiles and sanitaryware, will contain a lot of English ball clay. Ball clay is also used in ceramic floor tiles.

The 20th Century: from Depression to Remarkable Growth

The two World Wars and intervening Great Depression affected the industry badly. In America the ball clay deposits of Tennessee and Kentucky were opened up. However, after the Second World War the industry in Devon and Dorset enjoyed sustained growth. Post war reconstruction in the 1950s created demand in Britain and Northern Europe for clays for sanitaryware and tiles. This was followed in the 1960s and 1970s by growth in Italian and Spanish ceramic production. The 1970s and 1980s saw the emergence of new markets in the Middle and Far East, and in the 1990s further growth in ceramic tile production.

Since the 1950s ball clay has also been used in a wide range of non-ceramic applications, for example in coating fertiliser 'prills' (pellets), as a filler in rubber and linoleum and as an extender in animal feed stuffs. By 1970 annual sales had grown to 700,000 tonnes, and by 2000 to just over 1 million tonnes, more than 75% of which was exported – an achievement recognised in the several Queen's Awards for exports that were awarded to the clay companies.

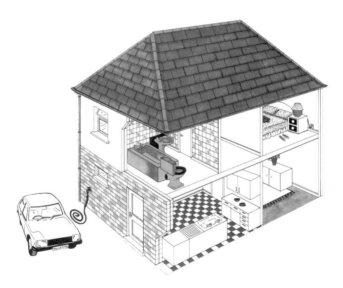

Ball clays are used in making many everyday articles, including – for the home: wall and floor tiles, wash basins, toilet bowls, plates, cups and saucers, linoleum, acoustic ceiling tiles, insulated electrical cables, pale coloured bricks and clay drainage pipes; for the car: windscreen wipers, spark plugs and engine mountings; for the garden: hoses and fertilisers.

4
The History of Ball Clay Production

Over the centuries there has been an evolution in the methods used to extract the valuable seams of ball clay. The methods varied slightly between the three areas of clay production. They are summarised below and then described in more detail.

Shallow trenches – from the 1600s

Small open pits – the natural development of shallow trenches, which grew in size when pumping techniques improved in the 19th century

Square pits – a development of small open pits in South Devon, enabling clays to be worked at a greater depth

Shaft mining (underground) – widely adopted from the second half of the 19th century. **Inclined shafts** (underground) – a variant of shaft mining adopted in North Devon from the end of the 19th century until the 1960s

Adit or Inclined tunnel mining (underground) – adopted in place of most shaft mining from the 1950s to the 1990s

Large scale opencast working – progressively replaced all underground mining during the second half of the 20th century: the only method after 1999.

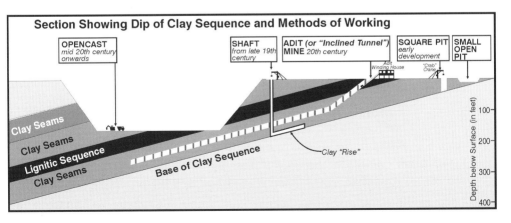

Section Showing Dip of Clay Sequence and Methods of Working

The Early Workings: Shallow Trenches

The tenant farmers who first found clay under their fields dug it with whatever farm implements came to hand. As time went by special techniques and tools were developed to work the clay. Despite some local variations, they were broadly similar in each of the three production areas.

The basic system was to dig a shallow trench. After removing unwanted overlying material called 'overburden' (or 'head' or 'ridding'), the 'claycutters' cut the exposed floor of clean plastic clay into a criss-cross pattern of 9 inch (23 cm) squares using heavy iron spades with blades 4 inch (10 cm) wide known as 'thirting' (or 'thwirting') irons. Following this, another claycutter used a weighty, ash-handled tool like a wide-bladed pick or mattock called a 'lumper' to undercut each square to a depth of 9 inches (23 cm) and lever out the resultant cube of clay weighing about 36 lbs (16.3 kg): 70 balls made a 'tally' of 22½ hundredweight (1.14 tonnes) – the measure used to pay the claycutters. The claycutters dipped their tools into a bucket of water to lubricate the cutting. A tool called a 'poge' – a curved iron spike set into a stout pole – was then used to pitch the cubes up the stepped sides of the pit to the surface and onto a packhorse or cart. A lighter version of the lumper known as a 'tubil' or 'tubal' was used to trim the working. In this way the whole floor area was removed to reveal the next layer for extraction.

Small Open Pits

As trenches widened they developed into open pits, which, although of some size considering the manual labour involved, were small by the standards of today. These remained the most economical way of extracting seams of clay that were close to the surface and not overlain by too much overburden. Neatly terraced slopes were a feature of the best of these pits. However, percolating groundwater and rainwater tended to cause open pits to flood, and their depth and area were therefore limited by the capacity of pumps to dispose of the water. Hand operated elm-barrelled pumps with a maximum lift of 15 feet (4.6 metres) were used originally, and although it was possible to have a series of pumps each with such a 'lift', it was not until the introduction of Cornish plunger pumps towards the end of the 19th century that open pits were developed to any great depth.

Lumper

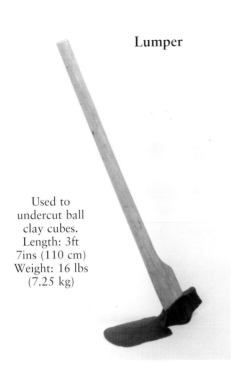

Used to undercut ball clay cubes.
Length: 3ft 7ins (110 cm)
Weight: 16 lbs (7.25 kg)

Thirting iron

Spade used to cut vertical sides of ball clay cube.
Length: 5ft (153 cm)
Weight: 10 lbs (4.5 kg)

Poge

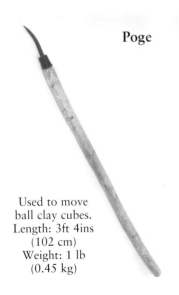

Used to move ball clay cubes.
Length: 3ft 4ins (102 cm)
Weight: 1 lb (0.45 kg)

Tubil

Used to cut clay underground and trim workings.
Length: 3 ft (90 cm)
Weight: 7 lbs (3.2 kg)

An open pit
showing cubes of
ball clay being cut
vertically using a
thirting iron
(central figure),
undercut using a
lumper (right
figure, partly
concealed) and
loaded onto a
wagon using a
poge (left figure),
c. 1930.

Clay cutters in a
neatly terraced
open pit at Meeth
with thirting irons,
lumpers and cans
of water to
lubricate the
cutting in the
1920s.

The Square Pit System

The ground water and rain that tended to cause open pits to flood also caused their soft sides to subside. To control subsidence, timber began to be used. This developed in South Devon into a system of excavating a sequence of 'square pits' that were timber lined and braced. After trial and error the optimum size was found to be 18 to 24 feet (5.5 to 7.3 metres) square. These square pits could then be dug to a depth of 50 feet (15.2 metres) with a series of pumping 'lifts' and ladders, but for a long time only the clay within the pit area was worked. About 12 feet (3.7 metres) of solid ground was left unworked between them, and the waste from one pit was used to backfill another.

To relieve the strenuous labour of manually lifting the clay and waste to the surface, a wooden crane of a type unique to the ball clay industry called a 'crab' would be erected beside the square pit to hoist the clay and waste to the surface in an elm bucket. The crab was a pivoting 'gallows' type crane held in place by two legs called 'tie backs'. Hand winches or horse drawn winches (known as 'whims') were used to raise and lower the buckets.

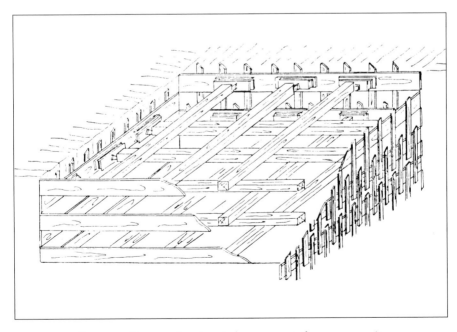

Cutaway diagram showing timber supports for a square pit.

A Devon & Courtenay square pit *c.* 1932 showing timber bracing, crab crane and stockpile of ball clay.

Each square pit produced a few hundred tons of the several types of clay through which the pit was sunk. Most were worked for just a few months until incoming water became too much for the hand pumps. Whilst shallow open pits remained the principal means of extracting stoneware clays, the square pit system was used to win the more valuable potters' clays that were typically found at a greater depth.

The Evolution of Underground Mining: Vertical Shafts

In South Devon the square pit system evolved by stages into true underground mining. First the claycutters started to rob a small area of the seam adjacent to the bottom of the pit – giving the pit a bell-like shape. Then short timbered levels were driven out from the base of the pit. This focused the operation on extracting a particular seam and on minimising the amount of material to be dug to reach it, which meant changing from digging a wide square pit to digging a vertical shaft wide enough simply to accommodate the bucket, ladders and pump lines.

Head of a shaft mine showing a 'crab' crane and an elevated timber ramp known as a 'high back'. The pivoted arm with a ring at the end, called a 'mouse', is a safety device to prevent the bucket being 'overwound', c. 1950.

Close up view of an elmwood bucket of dark ball clay being raised from the shaft at Mainbow near Newton Abbot. Note the separate compartments for hoisting and for pipelines and ladders, early 1960s.

23

By the 1870s underground shaft mining was enabling large quantities of deeper clays to be worked in all three production areas. By the end of the century the availability of Cornish pumps did away with the depth limitations of hand pumps. As a result, shafts could then be used to extract potters' clays at a depth of 50 to 150 feet (15 to 46 metres) – the greatest depth reached being 200 feet (61 metres) – whilst square pits and open pits remained in use to work the shallower stoneware clays.

Typical cross section dimensions of the shafts were 9 feet x 4½ feet (2.75 x 1.37 metres) and 13 feet x 6 feet (3.96 x 1.83 metres). The horizontal frames of larch supporting the sides of the shafts were separated vertically by timber 'studdles' between which boards and 'vraiths' or 'wreathes' of sedge grass or heather were rammed to hold back the sands through which the shafts were frequently driven. The shafts were divided into two compartments, one for hoisting by means of a crab and one for the access ladders and pump lines.

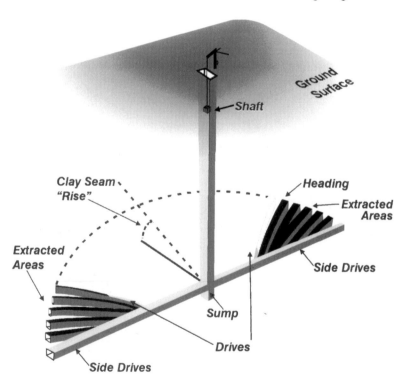

Diagram showing the underground mining of ball clay using a vertical shaft, drives and headings.

Having reached the desired seam and established a sump at the base of the shaft, two side drives (tunnels) supported by closely set green round larch timbers would be driven up to 100 feet (30 metres) in opposite directions from the base of the shaft through the level 'strike' of the seam. Traditionally, the seam would then be worked in a 'fan' shape by cutting further timbered drives from the base of the shaft, predominantly on the 'rise' side (where the seam sloped upwards). The drives were usually only 5½ feet (1.68 metres) high and 4 feet (1.22 metres) wide. Clay would squeeze through the timber supports, and a worked out drive would soon collapse under pressure from the ground above when the timber was withdrawn for re-use. The life of a shaft was rarely more than two to three years.

Because of the poor ventilation, normally only four miners at a time worked underground. A miner at each of two 'headings' cut the clay with a tubil. Another miner in each heading barrowed the clay down the drive to the base of the shaft using a heavy-duty elm wheelbarrow, typically carrying about 3 hundredweight (136 kg). The miners worked in what were, by modern standards, appallingly

Geoff Gibbs cutting clay with a pneumatic spader and Les Bickham loading it onto a rubber tyred wheelbarrow in Bill Tribble's shaft, Southacre, Preston Manor, Kingsteignton 1951. The larch roof timber is gradually giving way under pressure from the ground above. Other types of timber tend to give way suddenly.

25

unsafe conditions – by candlelight and sometimes ankle deep in water. In many mines there was the ever-present threat of a sudden water inrush and the ignition of 'fire damp' methane gases. Nevertheless, records of serious accidents (as distinct from singed eyebrows!) are surprisingly rare.

The 'top-ganger' – who was in charge of the gang working in the mine – operated the crab at the top of the shaft. The buckets carrying about 7 hundredweight (317 kg) of mined clay or waste were hoisted by wire ropes connected via overhead pulleys to steam engines or, later, DC electric motors in remote winch or drum houses that served several mines. Water wheels and turbines powered some Cornish pumps and hoists. The ganger controlled his rope hoist by means of a lever and long pull wire connected to a drum in the winch house, which he could engage against a continuously revolving shaft. Clay from the hoisted bucket was discharged into wagons. A 'top trammer' was responsible for the haulage of the wagons (by wire ropes from the winch house) up elevated timber ramps known as 'high backs' and the discharge of the clay and waste into separate heaps. The screeching of the ubiquitous wire ropes in their pulleys was the characteristic noise of the ball clay works.

Several companies established their own sawmills (replacing earlier saw pits) for the specialised cutting of the considerable quantities of mining timber that were required. One company even became involved in forestry. Skills such as those of the blacksmith (who forged the claycutters' tools), carpenter and wire rope splicer were essential in support of the claycutters. The claycutters' work – both in the pits and underground – was extremely arduous. Considerable physical strength was required to extract and man-handle the clay, often in soaking wet conditions. A miner's pay depended on the tonnage produced by him and his gang (so-called 'piecework'), but the pay was generally good so that, for generations, sons followed their fathers down the mines. Strength of character, prodigious cyder consumption and powerful tug-of-war teams were characteristic of the claycutters – as was rheumatism!

Inclined Shaft Mines

By the end of the 19th century shafts in North Devon were being sunk with a steep incline of 75 degrees from the horizontal, enabling wagons to run underground and be hauled to the surface on rails in the shafts. The tunnels of the North Devon Clay Co. were lined with bricks made at the adjacent Marland brickworks.

Inclined shafts at Peters Marland, North Devon c. 1900, showing head frames, mining wagons and stockpiles of clay adjacent to the three foot gauge railway.

20th Century Developments in Underground Mining and Opencast Workings

In the early 1900s steam generated DC electricity was introduced. Rail-mounted wagons hauled by wire ropes and discharging from 'high backs' were being widely used in open pits.

In the 1920s and 1930s some of the clay companies experimented with new working techniques and equipment. Advances were made by The Devon & Courtenay Clay Co. in the technique of sinking shafts through waterlogged sands, using techniques developed in the trenches of the First World War. This permitted hitherto inaccessible reserves to be worked. Devon & Courtenay in South Devon and the Meeth Clay Company in North Devon drove the first primitive 'adit'

Extracting clay from an open pit in North Devon in the 1930s. The traditional system of cutting the clay into cubes is still being used, but pneumatic spaders have been introduced to replace thirting irons for making the vertical cuts. Lumpers are still being used to undercut the cubes.

mines to follow seams from the bottom of existing pits. Steel arches were introduced in Meeth to support the main drives. In 1929 Newton Abbot Clays introduced the first steam excavator. Draglines were also introduced, potentially allowing the removal of greater thicknesses of overburden.

In the early 1930s, Newton Abbot Clays, followed by Devon & Courtenay and the North Devon Clay Co. introduced the first (very heavy!) hand-held pneumatic spaders to replace the thirting spade in the cutting of clays in open pits. Newton Abbot Clays experimented with a china clay-type 'sky tip' for waste (using an inclined railway), and, in 1937, introduced the first 3 cu. yard Muir Hill dumpers in their open pits.

Although the benefits of draglines, mechanical excavators, dumpers, pneumatic spaders and adits would later prove to be enormous, the depressed state of the industry between the Wars meant that little progress had been made in their adoption by 1946. In that year a Board of Trade Inquiry reported that: '. . . it would be difficult to find any industry in this country where there has been so

28

Extracting clay from an open pit in the 1950s. The clay is now being dug from a vertical face rather than the floor of the pit, using pneumatic spaders instead of thirting spades and lumpers. Rail mounted wagons are used to carry the clay up 'high backs' where it is tipped into heaps.

marked unawareness and such lack of initiative on the part of many producers to modern industrial change'. One of the Board of Trade's principal recommendations to increase productivity was to fit rubber tyres to the wheelbarrows used underground! The industry's problems were compounded by a shortage of manpower as a result of many able miners having been called up for military service, and the difficulty of recruiting ex-servicemen into such a backward industry.

This situation was soon to change remarkably, so that by 1969 one of the clay companies, Watts, Blake, Bearne & Co., was to be a recipient of the Queen's Award for technical innovation in underground mining.

In the open pits, diesel powered face shovels, dumpers and lighter pneumatic spaders became commonplace during the late 1940s and early 1950s, relieving the workers of the hardest physical labour.

Ruston Bucyrus 19-RB face shovel loading a Dennis Pax lorry from a stockpile at Whitepit, Preston Manor works, Kingsteignton, *c.* 1950.

Newton Abbot Clays – which had the problem of bringing clay out of constricted, steep-sided pits – installed 'Blondin' suspended wire rope systems to lift the clay out, but the company suffered a disaster in 1961 when one of its pits flooded, and the Blondins were subsequently replaced by dumpers.

In the 1960s bucket wheel excavators were introduced but were phased out in favour of hydraulic excavators that had the power and accuracy, in the hands of an experienced driver, to extract each clay seam to within a few inches of the bottom of the seam – minimising waste.

Underground, the lighter (but still heavy!) pneumatic spaders also became standard in the late 1940s, largely replacing the tubil.

Blondin aerial cableway used to raise buckets of ball clay from Newton Abbot Clays' open pits. The bucket is about to discharge from a side door into a waiting dumper, c. 1950.

Open pit mining at WBB's Southacre pit, Preston Manor, Kingsteignton, c. 1960, using pneumatic spaders and 3 cu. yard Muir Hill dumpers running on timber railway sleeper roadways.

Adit Mining

'Adit' or 'Inclined Tunnel' mining, which had been introduced in the 1930s, largely replaced vertical shaft mining during the 1950s and 1960s. Pairs of tunnels in South Devon and single tunnels in Dorset

An early adit mine driven into a clay seam in Devon & Courtenay's Little Bradley pit, Chudleigh Knighton. Fred 'Major' Harvey stands at the entrance. Late 1940s.

were driven into the ground at a shallow angle, following a particular seam from close to its outcrop to a considerable depth. A retreat method of working was then followed. Rails were laid in the drives so that wagons winched from a surface gantry could be used to haul the clay underground – replacing wheelbarrows – up to the surface. To maintain ground support over the years and in view of the increased tunnel size, the main drives were supported either by squared timbers or by steel arches or rings with timber backing boards. During the 1960s, leading up to the Queen's Award for technical innovation, the adit system was greatly improved with the introduction in South Devon of hydraulic mining machines (that greatly reduced the use of pneumatic spaders), of submersible pumps and of steel wagons with automatic tipping at the surface.

The longest adit drives extended underground for over half a mile

Part of early adit tunnel at Meeth showing steel roof supports, *c.* 1930.

WBB mining machine operated by Ivor Basset in an adit tunnel supported by steel arches. The machine had a cutting boom with rotating knives and a loading conveyor feeding finely cut clay into a wagon in the foreground, *c.* 1967.

(0.9 km) to a depth of up to 450 ft (137 metres). Individual adits in South Devon sustained an annual production of up to 25,000 tonnes for much of their 25-year lives.

The inherent greater safety of twin adit tunnels compared with a single mine shaft was augmented by the implementation of the 1954 Mines and Quarries Act, the banning of smoking and naked lights underground (ending the miners' traditional candle-heated fried breakfast) and the training of mines rescue and first aid teams.

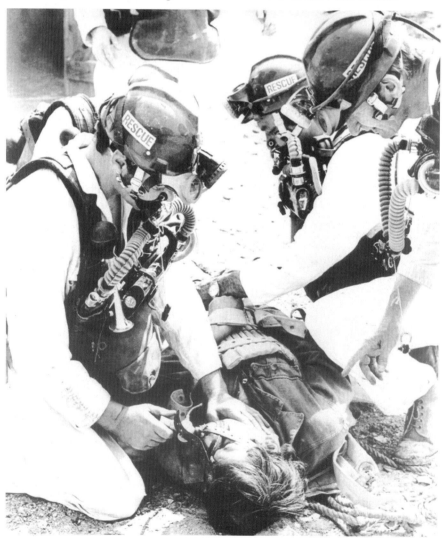

A mines rescue team practising their skills; fortunately these were rarely required.

Underground Mining Gives Way to Opencast Working

Due to its labour- and timber-intensive nature and the high cost of safety measures, underground mining was very expensive. As the mechanisation of opencast working progressed, underground mining became increasingly uneconomic, except to extract seams of the highest value that lay too deep for current opencast workings to reach. Having been the principal means of working for most of the industry's history, underground production was completely replaced by opencast working in North Devon by the mid 1970s and reduced steadily in South Devon and Dorset during the 1980s and 1990s when company sawmills were closed, until the last ball clay mines closed in 1999. Nowadays all production is from progressively larger and deeper pits using powerful hydraulic excavators and dumpers.

Systematic opencast working in Westbear Pit, North Devon in 1999 using hydraulic excavators and articulated dumpers running on movable concrete sleeper roads. The clay seams are being individually selected and taken by dumper to separate lump clay storage bays.

Processing

Traditionally, ball clays were sold 'as dug' in lumps or 'balls' – the 'potters'' clays usually being 'weathered' for several months in outside heaps. The clay producers did some very crude selection and mixing of what they perceived to be good and bad examples of individual clay types. The potters often bought in a variety of clays and mixed them together to their 'secret' formulae to make the pottery body they wanted.

This procedure continued virtually unchanged until the widespread adoption in the 1950s of the 'shredding' of clay into small pieces – a process first introduced in the 1930s that originally used mobile turnip cutting machines. Shredding makes handling much easier and, most importantly, enables the clay producers to blend together up to 20 or more different seams of clay, often from different production areas. This has helped them to compensate for the natural variation in individual seams and to produce blends that are consistent and meet their customers' specifications, especially for faster casting and faster firing.

The development of powdering, also during the 1950s, facilitated the sale of ball clays into non-ceramic applications such as rubber, fertilisers and animal feeds. Shredded clay is fed into an 'Atritor' mill together with hot air. The mill contains rotating shafts with pegs that break up the clay pieces. The hot air stream dries the feed clay from its natural 15–18% moisture down to a 2% moisture powder. The product is passed through an air classifier to remove any coarse particles and is then either bagged in paper sacks or delivered in bulk powder tankers.

The desire to produce controlled products for particular applications whilst optimising the use of marginal clays led in the 1970s to the development of ball clay refining using automated computer-controlled process equipment. Clays with too much lignite are made into a wet slurry and the excess lignite particles are removed by fine screens (sieves); clays with too much quartz sand are powdered and the excess silica removed by air separation. The resultant refined slurry and powder are mixed together into a paste, extruded in 'noodles' and dried for bulk handling. The product is also sold in a liquid or 'slurry' form.

Early shredding plant using a turnip shredder to reduce lump ball clay on the left to small pieces on the right.

A mobile shredder in use in the 1970s. The clay being tipped from the lorry consists of a specified number of bucket loads of several different types of lump clay. The clay is being thrown by the shredder into the storage bay. This process homogenises the mixture and is essential for the creation of controlled clay blends.

Filling 50 kg-paper sacks with clay that
has been dried and pulverised to a fine
powder, *c*. 1960.

For many years ball clay companies produced 'prepared bodies'. These are the various mixtures of minerals (such as ball and china clays, silica, feldspar etc.) that normally the potter prepares and then shapes, decorates and fires. WBB also produced 'calcined' clays – pelletised ball clays fired in a rotary kiln and then ground down and incorporated in a pottery body. Having already been fired, calcined clays reduce the expansion and contraction of the body when it is fired as a ceramic.

Now at the beginning of the 21st century, around 75% of ball clay production is sold in shredded and blended form, almost 10% in powdered form and about 15% is refined. Less than 1% is sold 'as dug'. Process control has become an essential skill of ball clay production.

Powdered ball clay in paper sacks stacked on wooden pallets being shrink-wrapped and then loaded onto a lorry, 1996.

The East Golds processing site at Newton Abbot in 2000 showing ball clay refining plants and product storage in the foreground, powdering plant at upper centre and a lignite processing plant for horticultural applications on the upper right.

Employment Relationships

Enormous changes in working methods occurred in the ball clay industry in the second half of the 20th century – especially during the 1960s. Highly regarded 'productivity agreements' provided for these changes to be accompanied by the adoption of progressive employment practices, for which the companies became well known. These included the replacement of piecework and overtime pay systems by 'staff' conditions of employment for all employees, with fixed rates of pay and hours of work, pensions and sick pay. They were combined with systematic training and great emphasis both on health and safety, and on employee communication and involvement. The success of these arrangements depended on the high degree of trust that developed between management and employees.

The development of these progressive employment practices created an environment in which the workforce was willing to respond positively to the changes taking place and to develop their skills through the training opportunities offered. As the physical demands on the workforce diminished, the roles of maintenance fitters and electricians became more important. Production increasingly required the close collaboration of multi-skilled teams of geologists, drillers, surveyors and quality control chemists working closely with process engineers, ceramists and technical sales personnel to assess how best to fulfil customers' needs with the complex sequence of clay seams in the ground and use of the appropriate processing facilities.

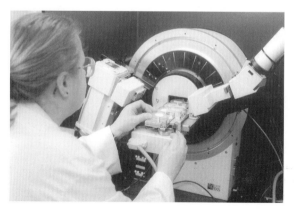

An X-ray diffractometer being used to identify the minerals, such as kaolinite, illite and quartz, in a sample of ball clay. This and other chemical and physical tests are carried out to monitor the properties of each seam of clay.

5
Ball Clay and Transport

The history of ball clay is bound up with the development of canals, railways and shipping which have all played a vital part in transporting clays economically to customers.

Packhorses and, later, horses and carts were the only methods of getting clay away from the pits until the advent of railways and lorries. However, it was only practical to use packhorses and carts over short distances. Fortunately, each of the ball clay deposits was reasonably close to a port from which the clay could be transported by vessel to such ports as London, Bristol and Liverpool and Runcorn on the Mersey (for the Staffordshire potteries via the Bridgewater Canal and Josiah Wedgwood's Trent & Mersey Grand Trunk Canal), as well as continental European ports.

Amos Hewings with J. Vallance's horse and cart at Teignbridge loaded with ball clay en route to Teignbridge clay cellars on the Stover Canal, 1906.
(*Photo courtesy Richard Harris*)

The Stover Canal

Above
Barges at the Teignbridge clay cellars on the Stover Canal waiting to be moved to Teignmouth, *c.* 1920.

Left
Early photograph of loaded clay barges under sail on the Stover Canal with their characteristic square 'Viking' sails rigged.

Below
The tug Heron towing loaded clay barges down the Whitelake Channel from the Stover Canal to the River Teign, *c.* 1920.

Falke loading clay from barges at Teignmouth in the 1920s.

In South Devon the port for ball clay was Teignmouth. The first recorded shipment from Teignmouth was to London in 1680, shortly before William of Orange was proclaimed king in Newton Abbot in 1688. Originally, packhorses carried the clay from the pits to Hackney quay at the head of the Teign estuary where it was either loaded directly into small sailing vessels or taken by barge (or 'lighter') to larger sailing vessels moored in Teignmouth harbour.

The high cost of the packhorse journey was greatly reduced by the construction of the Stover Canal from the Teign estuary to Teigngrace by James Templer II in 1790-1792, and of the Hackney Canal from Hackney quay into Kingsteignton for Lord Clifford in 1843. Clay cellars were built on both canals for the storage of clay prior to shipment. At about this time the Earl of Devon's 'Devon Wharf' (now the 'Town Quay') in Newton Abbot started to be used to load barges with clay from his newly opened Decoy pits. The barges had characteristic square 'Viking' sails but were latterly towed in the estuary by the steam tug 'Kestrel' and finally by the paraffin engine tug 'Heron'.

The construction of the Moretonhampstead branch railway line in 1867, with sidings at Teignbridge, East Golds and Heathfield, enabled the railway to be used increasingly to supply domestic

Unloading ball clay into rail wagons at the East Golds sidings
of Newton Abbot Clays in the 1930s.

customers. However, the introduction of lorries, enabling clay to be carried far more economically than by cart and barge, led to use of the canals ceasing in the 1930s and of the railway in the 1980s.

The main outlets for ball clay in North Devon were Bideford Quay and, for a period, Fremington Quay on the Taw estuary. The first recorded shipments of tobacco pipe clay from Bideford were in the 1650's. However, after the initial century or more of activity, the high cost of the packhorse journey from the pits at Peters Marland (relative to transport costs in South Devon and Dorset) seems to have led to the closure of the works in the early 19th century. The situation was improved by the construction in 1827 of Lord John Rolle's Canal up to Torrington. It was transformed in 1881 when the eminent railway engineer, J.B. Fell, commissioned by Marland Brick & Clay Works Ltd., completed a 3-foot (91cm) gauge light railway from Peters Marland to Torrington – including a remarkable wooden viaduct over the River Torridge. Eventually, in 1925, a standard gauge railway was built along the course of the narrow gauge one, enabling clays from both Peters Marland and Meeth to be shipped out of the rail-connected Fremington Quay until the closure of the line to clay traffic in 1982. Now, once again, Bideford Quay is regularly used for clay shipments.

Three foot gauge North Devon railway at Peters Marland in the 1920s, alongside the headgear of inclined shafts. The Fletcher Jennings locomotive came from a breakwater scheme at St Helier in 1908.

Ball clay loading at Fremington Quay with a steam crane on standard gauge rails, *c.* 1930.

Poole Quays. Clay being loaded from barges into vessels for the Mersey and other ports. Late 19th century.

Poole has been important for the shipment of ball clays from Dorset since the beginning of the 17th century. Until the 19th century the clay was carried by packhorse or cart to Wareham Quay on the river Frome or a loading point on the edge of Poole Harbour. From there it was barged to quays at Poole and loaded on sea-going vessels for shipment to Runcorn, London and other ports. In 1805-6 Benjamin Fayle built the first railway in Dorset: a pioneering cast iron 'plateway' along which horses hauled wagons of clay from his pits at Norden to Middlebere Pier. In 1907 'Fayle's Tramway', a 3 foot 9 inch (114 cm) gauge railway from Newton to Goathorn Pier using steam locomotives, was extended to Norden and the plateway was closed. The other producers, Pike Brothers, operated a 2 foot 8 inch (81 cm) gauge railway from Furzebrook to Wareham Quay. From its arrival in 1884 the main line LSWR line was used to transport clay to domestic customers. The narrow gauge railways continued until 1954 when the two companies amalgamated and transferred local movements to road transport.

Nowadays lorries are the only means of transporting ball clays to customers within the UK, notably the concentration around Stoke-on-Trent. Clay for European and Mediterranean markets is generally hauled by lorry to Teignmouth, Bideford or Poole, whilst clays for other parts of the world are shipped in containers that are filled at the clay works and transported by lorry to container ports such as Southampton, Felixstowe and Thamesport.

Steam locomotive *Secondus* at Furzebrook in Dorset. This locomotive was used by Pike Brothers from 1874 to 1953 and still survives – the only extant Birmingham loco. Note the cowcatcher!
(*Photo courtesy of Eric Shepherd*)

Clay being loaded into the hold of a vessel at Teignmouth, *c*. 1985. The lorry tips the clay onto an enclosed conveyor to minimise dust. For many years Teignmouth has been the major port for ball clay shipments.

6
How The Clay Companies Evolved

For most of the 300-year history of the ball clay industry the great landowners owned much of the land on which the clay was worked. This was especially true in South Devon. In Kingsteignton the landowners were the Bishop of Salisbury and the Cliffords of Ugbrooke. In Newton Abbot they were the Earls of Devon and around Stover they were the Templers and the Dukes of Somerset. Whilst they granted mining leases over their lands to clay merchants they generally avoided getting involved directly in the business of mining and selling the clay – although both James Templer II and Lord Clifford were evidently sufficiently satisfied with the benefit they derived from their clay leases to build the canals mentioned earlier.

Some of the most enterprising clay merchants acquired the freehold of important clay bearing land from the traditional landowners – often in addition to having long mining leases. The Greenings in North Devon controlled parts of what became the Marland North Devon clay works as early as the 1650s. The Pikes (from Chudleigh) followed in Dorset over 100 years later, leasing land from the Bond and Calcraft estates, and in 1760 formed Pike Brothers, probably the first partnership of clay merchants. Benjamin Fayle followed in Dorset, establishing Benjamin Fayle and Company in 1795.

In South Devon, the Watts family acquired key landholdings and a valuable lease from the Bishop of Salisbury, which they brought into a partnership with Whiteway in 1796. Serious competition started for Whiteway, Watts & Co. in 1856 when The Devon and Courtenay Clay Company was formed with a lease of the Decoy property from the Earl of Devon. In 1861 the Watts family broke away from the Whiteways and brought their extensive clay properties into a partnership with Blake and Bearne, forming Watts, Blake, Bearne and Company Whiteway, Watts & Co. then became simply Whiteway and Company.

In North Devon, William Wren, a descendant of Greening, brought life back into the industry there by establishing the Marland Brick & Clay Works Ltd. in 1879 – probably the first limited liability company in the ball clay industry – and built the vital Marland light

A Bideford ware salt glazed bowl, ten inches in diameter, made using North Devon ball clay. The inscribed rim shows it was made in 1727 for a member of the Greening family of Bideford who were involved with North Devon clay production from the 17th to the end of the 19th century.

railway from the works to Torrington. The North Devon Clay Company Ltd. took over the business on its incorporation in 1893.

Many new companies were started or became involved in ball clay production just before or after the First World War, notably, in South Devon, Hexter and Budge Ltd, the Newton Abbot Clays Ltd., the Mainbow Clay Company Ltd., the Pochin Ball Clay Company Ltd, and the London, Australian & General Exploration Company Ltd. and, with the arrival of the standard gauge railway in North Devon, the Meeth (North Devon) Clay Company Ltd.

After the Second World War there were more than 15 ball clay producing companies – most of them weak either financially or in terms of the reserves that they controlled. By 1969 they had been consolidated by a series of mergers and acquisitions into just two groups, Watts, Blake, Bearne & Co. (WBB) and English China Clays (ECC). These companies were able to rationalise the patchwork of freehold ownerships – allowing larger pits to be developed – and modernise production.

The Pochin Ball Clay Company and the Mainbow Clay Company had joined what became ECC before the Second World War. During the 1950s ECC acquired the London, Australian company and Hexter and Budge. There followed in the 1960s a 'scramble' between WBB and ECC to acquire the other companies. ECC acquired Meeth (North Devon) and Pike Brothers, Fayle (a merger of the two Dorset companies), operating its ball clay business under the name of Hexter and Budge and then as ECC Ball Clays. Following these acquisitions, ECC's share of UK ball clay production was about 40%.

The parent company, English China Clays Plc, is now owned by Imerys SA of France and is known as Imerys Minerals Ltd. Imerys already owned ball clay production companies in France when it acquired ECC and has subsequently acquired ball clay production companies in the USA, Thailand and Poland.

During the 1960s WBB under Claude Pike became a public company, and acquired Devon and Courtenay (which had itself acquired Whiteway & Co.), Newton Abbot Clays and the North Devon Clay Company. As a result, WBB became the largest UK ball clay producer with a share of about 60% of the total.

From the mid 1970s to the mid 1990s WBB took advantage of the UK industry's technical advancement to became the world's leading producer of various types of ball clays, acquiring or setting up ball clay production or processing operations in Germany (West and East), France, Thailand, China, the USA, Portugal, Netherlands, Indonesia and Ukraine. Since 1999 WBB has been wholly owned by SCR Sibelco SA of Belgium and has been joined with the former Hepworths sand division based in Cheshire to become WBB Minerals. Many of WBB's overseas operations are now controlled by other companies in the Sibelco group.

Flooded former clay pits have made the Bovey Basin one of the most important areas for dragonflies and damselflies in Britain. This new pond at the former Little Bradley clay works was created in 1991 to replace habitats threatened by reworking. Of the 37 British species of dragonfly 21 have been seen at this pond and at least 13 species have been known to breed here.

7
Ball Clay And The Environment

Old ball clay workings often show an astonishing biodiversity that is
far greater than existed on the farmland before the working began.
When – in the past – the old, shallow workings were finished
the land was either restored to farmland or it was abandoned.
In the latter case the pits themselves quickly filled with water and the
surrounding areas soon re-vegetated. This resulted in the creation of
havens for many species of increasingly rare flora and fauna –
notably dragonflies and butterflies. Several of the old workings have
become nature reserves managed by the Devon Wildlife Trust and
have been the subject of TV films by Peter Scott and Andrew Cooper.
Others have become ponds and lakes for amenity, coarse fishing and
boating. The best examples are the famous 'Blue Pool' near Wareham
and Decoy Lake in Newton Abbot, which also have nature trails
open to visitors.

Since the merging of the 15 ball clay companies into two by the
end of the 1960s, workings have been rationalised and fewer, much
larger, pits have been developed. The industry was amongst the first
to take measures to mitigate the inevitable impact that its workings
have on the environment, and tip design and landscaping continue to
improve within the framework of long term plans agreed with the
local planning authorities.

In far-sighted recognition of ball clay's national importance and
scarcity, special planning safeguards against the sterilisation of ball
clay reserves by housing and other development have been in place
since 1953. However the balance to be struck between the interests of
working an internationally rare and useful mineral where it lies and
preserving the existing local environment has become an increasingly
prominent issue, especially in Dorset, where the deposits lie in areas
with some of the highest landscape and nature designations.

With annual ball clay production at the beginning of the 21st
century running at over one million tonnes, and with the enormous
deposits, particularly in the Bovey Basin, able to sustain production
for at least another 50 years, this debate is set to continue.

8
Further Reading

'North Devon Clay: the History of an Industry and its Transport' by M.J. Messenger (1982 Twelveheads Press, Truro ISBN 0 906 294 061)

'The Clay Mines of Dorset 1760-1960' by Pike Bros, Fayle & Co. Ltd. (1960 Harley Publishing Co. Ltd, London)

'The Potters' Field: a History of the South Devon Ball Clay Industry' by L.T.C. Rolt (1974 David & Charles, Newton Abbot ISBN 0 7153 6504 5). Some copies available through the Ball Clay Heritage Society.

'Ball Clay': Mineral Dossier No. 11, (1975 British Geological Survey, Keyworth. ISBN 0 1151 0835 1).

'The Beginnings of the Devonshire Ball-Clay Trade' by J.A. Bulley (1955 The Transactions of the Devonshire Association, Vol. lxxxvii, pp 191-204).

Visit of the Devonshire Association to the North Devon Clay Company at Peters Marland in 1899. This train is hauled by the locomotive Marland bought new in 1883, which worked until 1925.

The Blue Pool at Furzebrook, near Wareham a tourist attraction for over 60 years based on a ball clay pit started by Pike Brothers c.1840. *Image courtesy Miss. Jennifer Barnard*

Visit by pupils of All Saints Marsh Primary School, Newton Abbot to WBB's Preston Manor Works, Kingsteignton in Industry Year, 1986

Illustrations on top of back cover

Left: A Common Blue butterfly for which old clay workings are a favoured refuge.
Centre: Wedgwood Queen's ware jug of 1786 in cream coloured earthenware.
        Image by courtesy Wedgwood Museum Trust, Barlaston, Staffordshire.
Right: Excavator working a ball clay seam 2002.

The Ball Clays of Devon and Dorset

It is surprising to most people that Devon and Dorset have some of the world's most important deposits of a mineral - ball clay - that is used in the making of cups, saucers, wash basins, tiles and other articles that they use everyday.

Starting in the 17th century the history of ball clay production is bound up with tobacco pipe manufacture, fine pottery by Wedgwood and others, architectural ceramics, and the building of canals and railways to transport the clays.

Over the centuries, unique implements and mining methods were developed to win these unusual clays that owe their plastic, white-firing properties to a rare combination of geological conditions. Today, this important export industry producing about one million tonnes annually is not without environmental controversy!

ISBN 1-90014-730-0

9 781900 147309

Price £3.99
Cornish Hillside Publication